THE FABER GRADED
ROCK&POP SERIES
GRADE Initial-1

Guitar SONGBOOK

GW00644920

CONTENTS

© 2013 by Faber Music Ltd
First published by Faber Music Ltd in 2013
Bloomsbury House
74 – 77 Great Russell Street
London WC1B 3DA

Music arranged by Tom Fleming
Edited by Lucy Holliday
Designed by Chloë Alexander
Audio produced, mixed & mastered by Tom Fleming
Guitar & Bass: Tom Fleming
Vocals: Bo Walton
Drums: George Double

Printed in England by Caligraving Ltd
All rights reserved

This paper is 100% recyclable

ISBN10: 0-571-53720-0
EAN13: 978-0-571-53720-4

To buy Faber Music publications or to find out about the
full range of titles available, please contact your local
music retailer or Faber Music sales enquiries:

Faber Music Limited, Burnt Mill, Elizabeth Way,
Harlow CM20 2HX
Tel: +44 (0)1279 82 89 82
Fax: +44 (0)1279 82 89 83
sales@fabermusic.com
fabermusic.com

CD

FABER ff **MUSIC**

HINTS & TIPS

21st Century Breakdown

Green Day is an American punk rock band, and this is the title song from their eighth studio album and their biggest selling record to date. Their sound is similar to the first wave of punk bands that came on the music scene in the 1970s, and they often stick to the formula of fast and catchy three-chord songs.

- A light crunch tone using the bridge pickup will probably work best here – enough to give a rock feel, but not so much that the full major/minor chords sound muddy.

- Take care not to strike extraneous open bass strings (alternatively they may be muted using the left-hand thumb).

- Pay attention to the timing of the syncopated chords on the second half of the second beat – don't rush.

Be-Bop-A-Lula

Gene Vincent (born Vincent Eugene Craddock) was one of the very first rock 'n' roll artists, and 'Be-Bop-A-Lula' was his biggest hit, released in 1956. This song is a classic example of the *Rockabilly* style, which is a fusion of rock 'n' roll and country (hillbilly) music.

- Most of the guitar part uses the classic 'sixth shuffle' pattern found in so much 50s rock 'n' roll.

- Light palm muting may work well but is not essential. Take care only to strike the pair of strings in use for each part of the pattern.

- This pattern may be played using down-strokes only, but a fluid swung feel will be more easily achieved using down-strokes on the beat and upstrokes on the offbeat.

For What It's Worth

This song was **Buffalo Springfield**'s only major hit, and was written as a plea for tolerance after American police used heavy-handed methods to try to stop an anti-Vietnam war demonstration in 1966. The song also became an anthem for students who were unhappy at that time with the Nixon government.

- This chord section will probably sound best using a clean, warm sound (neck pickup or middle position).

- Take care not to strike unwanted open bass strings (for example the low E and A strings when playing the D chord). The quavers (eighth notes) on beat four should be played using a down/up motion.

Proud Mary

'Proud Mary' was **Creedence Clearwater Revival**'s first big hit, introducing the world to their mix of Southern Creole music (American folk roots music from the Louisiana area), rhythm 'n' blues and rockabilly. In 1970, Ike & Tina Turner covered the song, and it has since become one of Turner's signature tunes.

- For this part to sound fluid, a constant down/up motion is required. The rests in the main strumming pattern fall on the beat, so there should be a down-strum here, but missing the strings instead of striking them.

- The chord pattern could easily sound louder than the single line in the intro and outro, so it is important to play the latter energetically, but to relax somewhat when playing the chords.

Rock N Roll Queen

Indie rock band **The Subways** burst onto the UK scene in 2005, and 'Rock N Roll Queen' became an instant party anthem and is a rock festival favourite.

- The rock feel required relies on constant down-strokes as indicated; try not to tense the wrist any more than you have to.

- Palm muting in the verse helps to keep the volume down and produce a musical contrast when moving into the chorus, which needs to be louder and fuller.

Rockaway Beach

The Ramones was one of America's leading punk rock bands, bringing with them the fashion of leather jackets, ripped jeans and loads of attitude. Their musical style was a reaction against the heavily produced rock & pop bands of the 50s and 60s, so they created a very raw sound and short snappy songs.

- Aim for a very even quaver (eighth-note) feel here, with as little accenting as possible.

- The rhythm changes subtly between verse and chorus, producing an effective musical variation.

- The rests in the outro should be observed (don't let the chords ring through them), and take care not to rush here.

Runaway Train

The video for **Soul Asylum**'s 'Runaway Train' is all about young people who have run away from home, showing various images of children who have run away or in trouble for one reason or another. The song and video highlighted the problem in the UK and America of homeless and troubled children.

- This part should be played using a clean sound, aiming to sound as much as possible like an acoustic guitar.

- A continuous down/up motion is essential when playing the main syncopated pattern here: a 'phantom' down-stroke (missing the strings) on beat three is crucial.

Sunny Afternoon

London band **The Kinks** is seen as one of the most influential British groups of all time, selling millions of records and countless hit singles. This song is one of their finest and actually knocked The Beatles' 'Paperback Writer' from the number one spot in the charts.

- The *staccato* notes in the intro and outro should be played using left-hand muting (release finger pressure after playing the note).

- In the strumming pattern, the quaver (eighth-note) pairs should be played slightly swung (down/up), and beats 2 and 4 should be emphasised slightly.

- The offbeat *staccato* chords in the chorus should be fairly short, though not aggressive, and you will probably need a combination of left- and right-hand muting to stop them ringing through the rests.

Take It Easy

The group the **Eagles** is the king of the American country rock sound, and also one of the most successful bands of the 1970s. Their songs have great melodies, tight harmonies, and a brilliantly relaxed feel to them.

- Aim for a clean sound for this song.

- The single line work should be articulated clearly; it is important to lay back a little to play the rhythm as this could easily become too loud in relation to the lead work.

- Aim for a fluid quaver (eighth-note) pulse, using continuous down/up motion and be careful not to play unwanted bass strings.

The Twist

American songwriter **Chubby Checker** is widely known for his version of this song, which inspired the massive 60s' dance craze The Twist. It's a rock 'n' roll classic and one of the most popular American singles of all time.

- Rhythmic accuracy is important here.

- The *staccato* 'stab' chords should be played accurately on the beat. Be careful not to play the stabs on the second half of beat 2 early, as this could easily sound rushed.

21ST CENTURY BREAKDOWN

Words and Music by Billie Joe Armstrong, Frank E. Wright III and Michael Pritchard

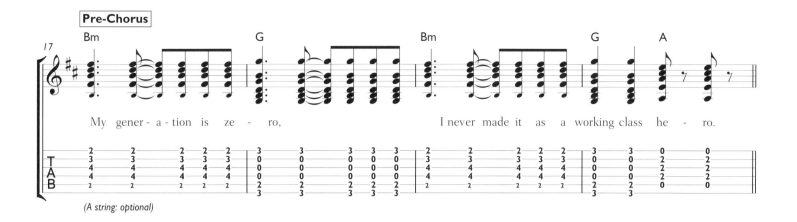

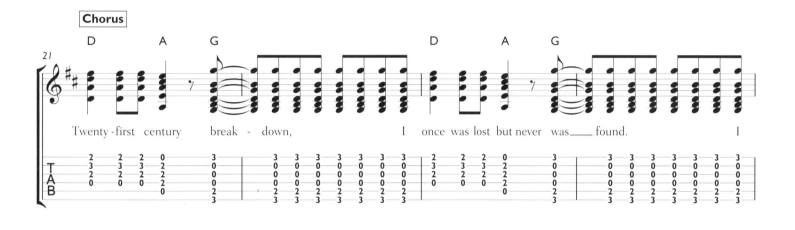

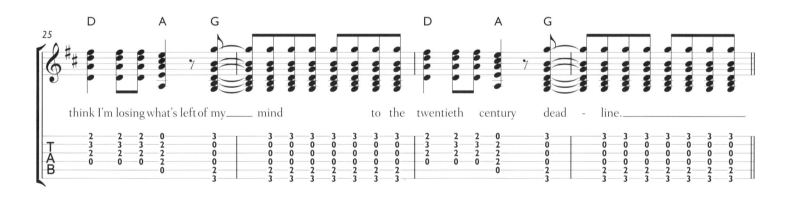

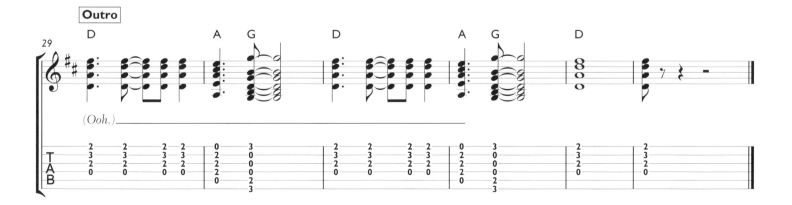

BE-BOP-A-LULA

Words and Music by Tex Davis and Gene Vincent

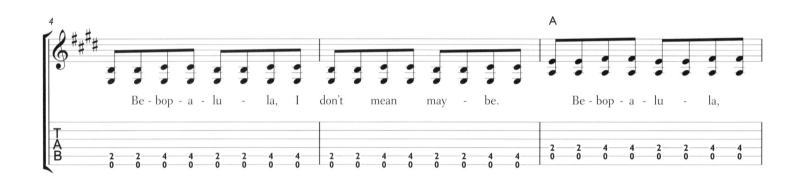

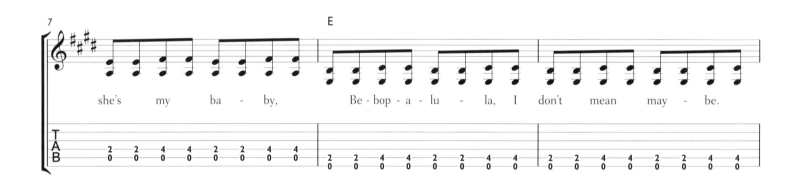

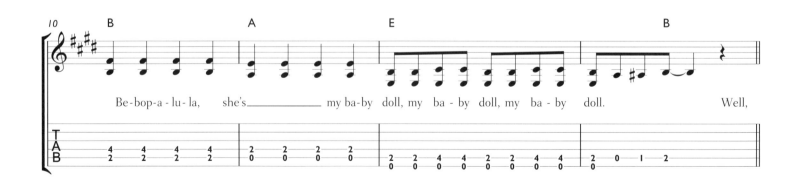

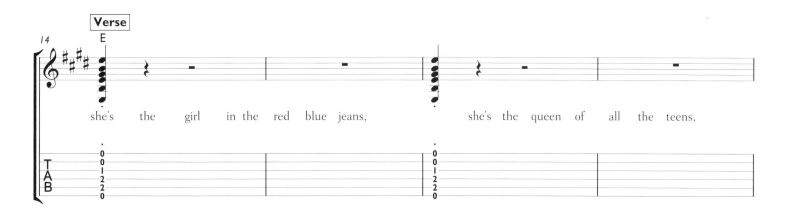

Verse

14 E

she's the girl in the red blue jeans, she's the queen of all the teens,

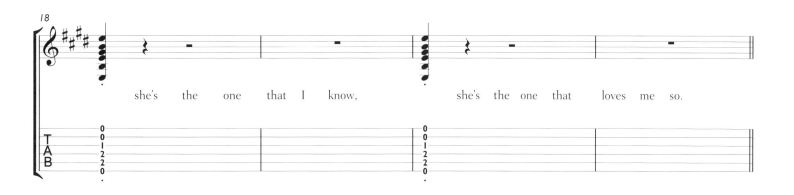

18

she's the one that I know, she's the one that loves me so.

Outro

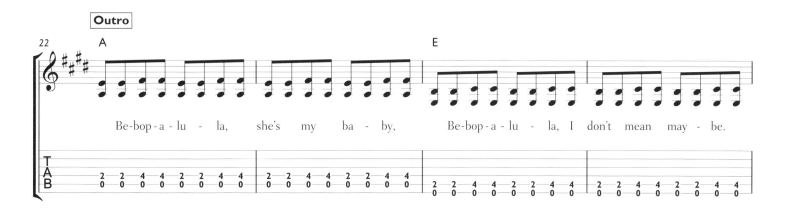

22 A E

Be-bop-a-lu-la, she's my ba-by, Be-bop-a-lu-la, I don't mean may-be.

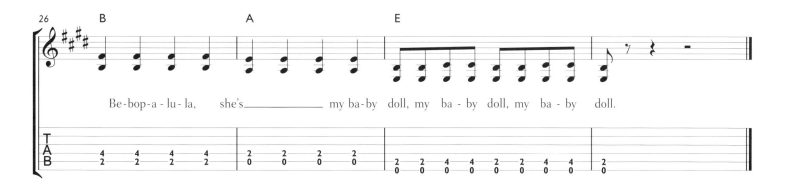

26 B A E

Be-bop-a-lu-la, she's_____ my ba-by doll, my ba-by doll, my ba-by doll.

FOR WHAT IT'S WORTH

Words and Music by Stephen Stills

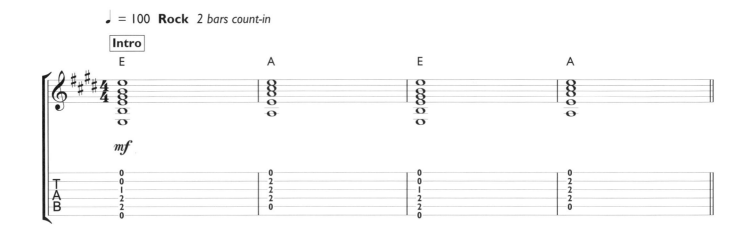

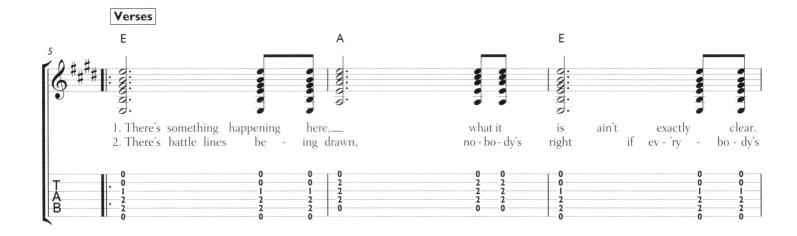

1. There's something happening here,___ what it is ain't exactly clear.
2. There's battle lines be - ing drawn, no - bo - dy's right if ev - 'ry - bo - dy's

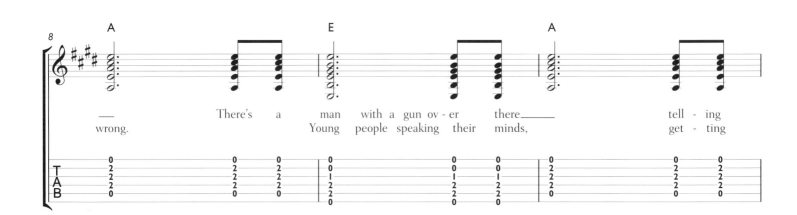

wrong. ___ There's a man with a gun ov - er there___ tell - ing
Young people speaking their minds, get - ting

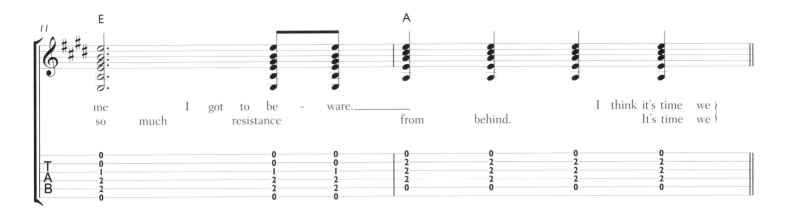

me   I got to be - ware._____ from   behind.   I think it's time   we)
so   much   resistance   It's time   we)

Chorus

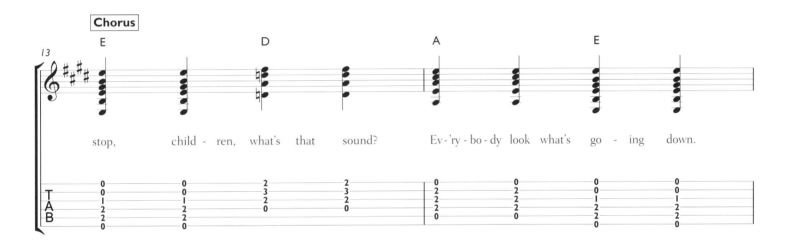

stop,   child - ren, what's that   sound?   Ev-'ry - bo - dy look what's go - ing   down.

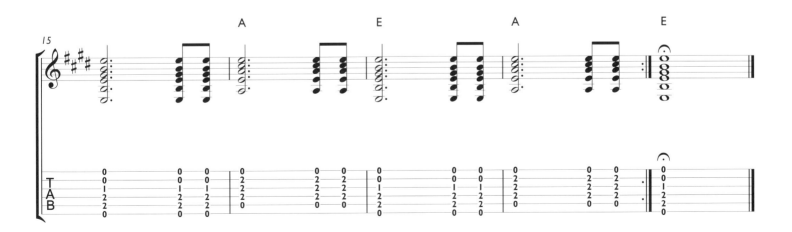

PROUD MARY

Words and Music by John Fogerty

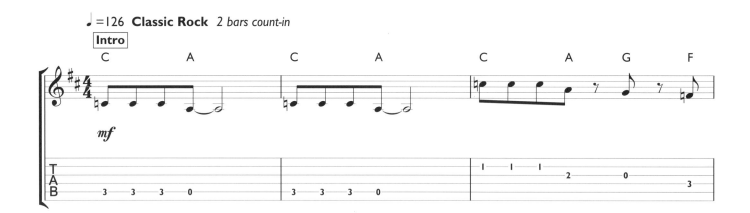

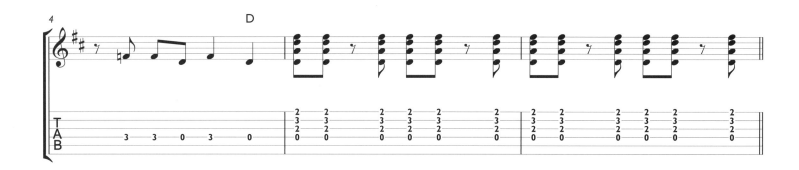

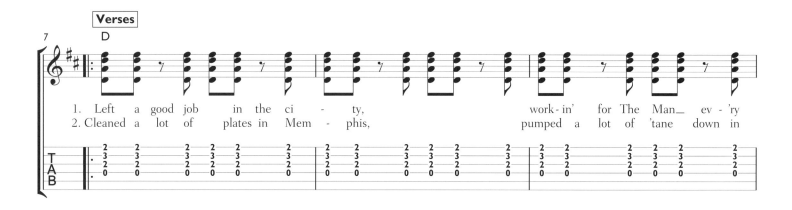

1. Left a good job in the ci - ty, work-in' for The Man ev'-ry
2. Cleaned a lot of plates in Mem - phis, pumped a lot of 'tane down in

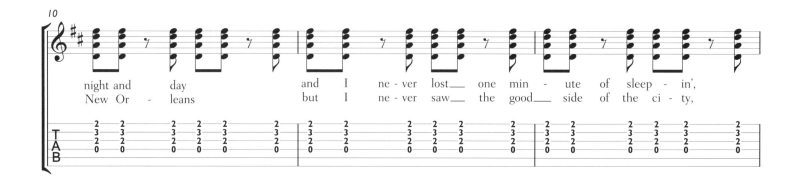

night and day and I ne - ver lost one min - ute of sleep - in',
New Or - leans but I ne - ver saw the good side of the ci - ty,

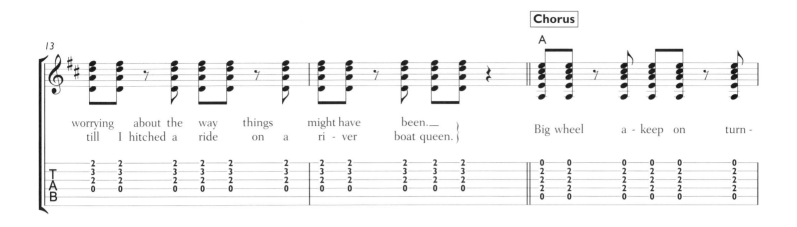

worrying   about the   way   things   might have   been.___
till   I   hitched a   ride   on   a   ri - ver   boat queen.

Big wheel   a - keep on   turn-

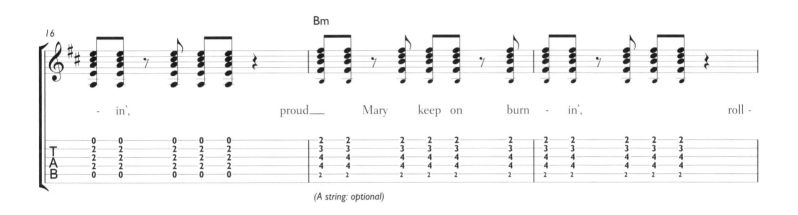

- in',   proud___   Mary   keep on   burn - in',   roll -

(A string: optional)

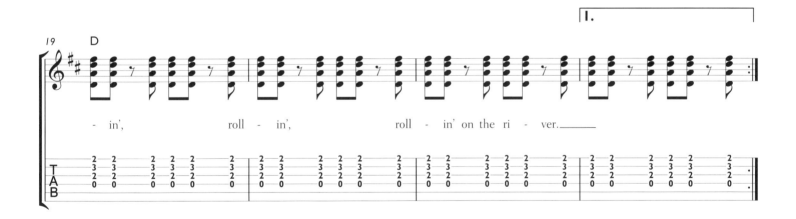

- in',   roll - in',   roll - in' on the ri - ver._____

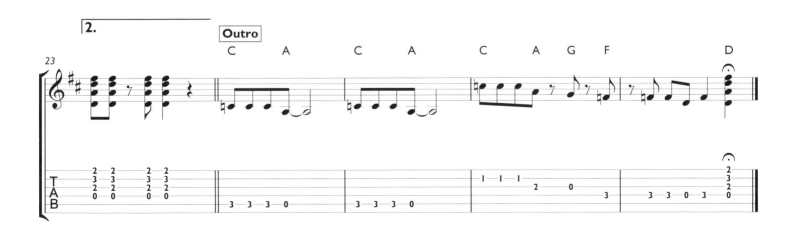

Demo
BT

ROCK N ROLL QUEEN

Words by Billy Lunn
Music by The Subways

♩ = 144 **Indie Rock**   *2 bars count-in*

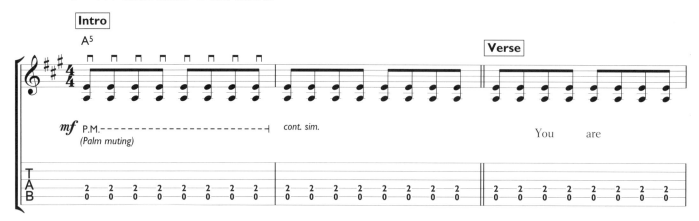

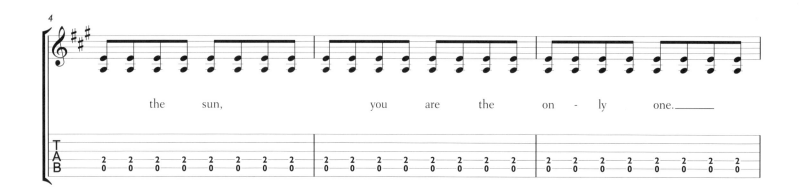

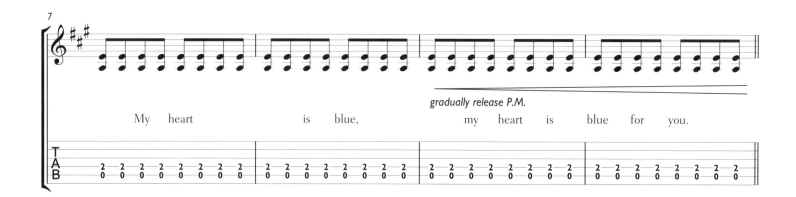

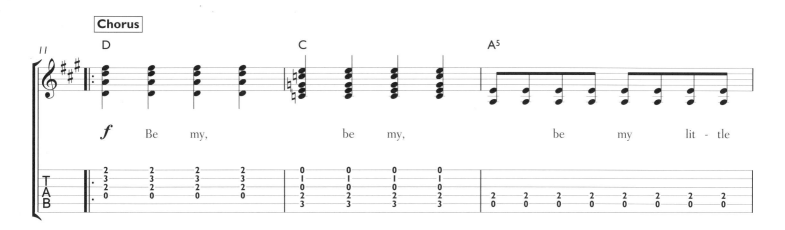

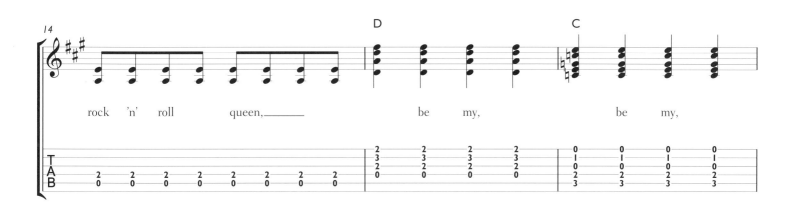

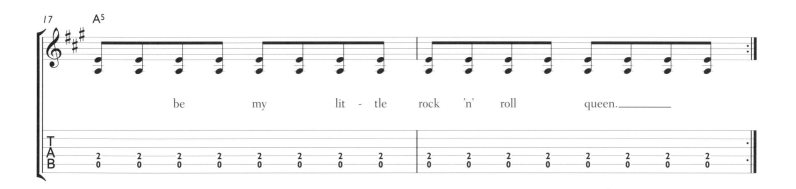

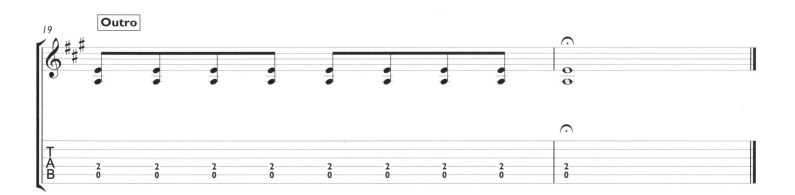

ROCKAWAY BEACH

Words and Music by Joey Ramone, Johnny Ramone,
Dee Dee Ramone and Tommy Ramone

♩ = 150 **Punk Rock** *2 bars count-in*

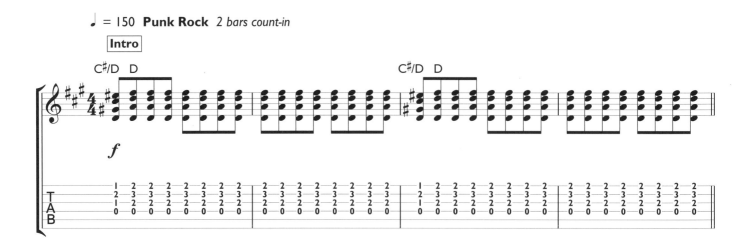

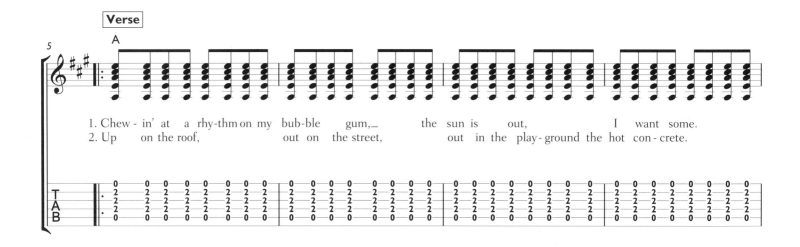

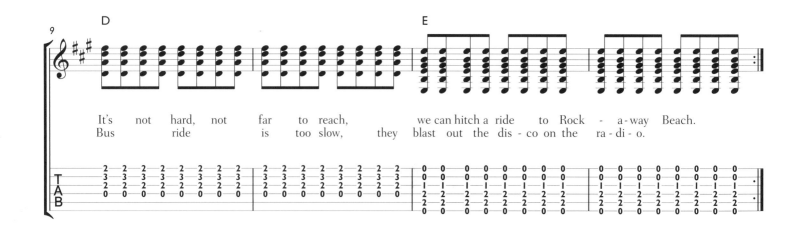

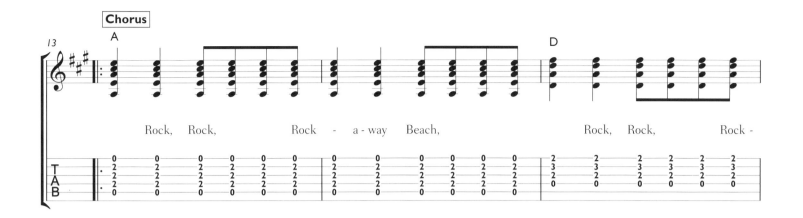

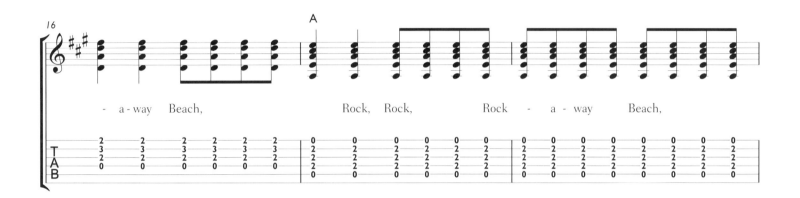

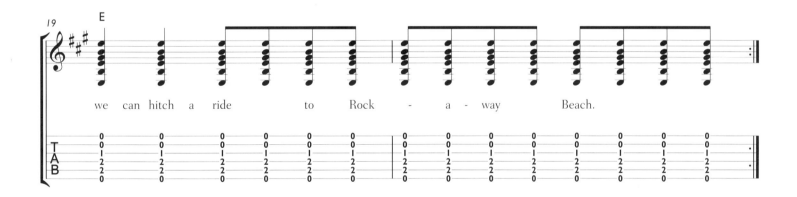

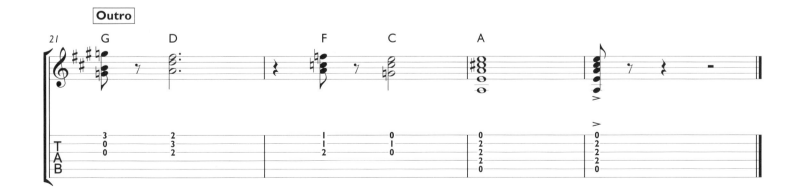

Demo
BT

RUNAWAY TRAIN

Words and Music by David Pirner

♩ = 121 **Moderately** *2 bars count-in*

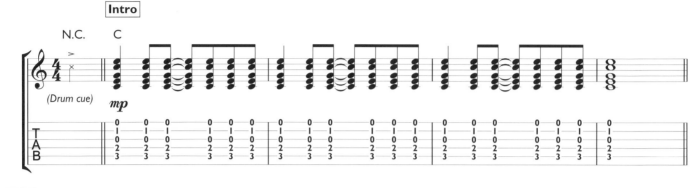

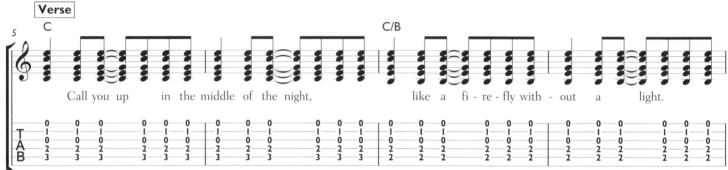

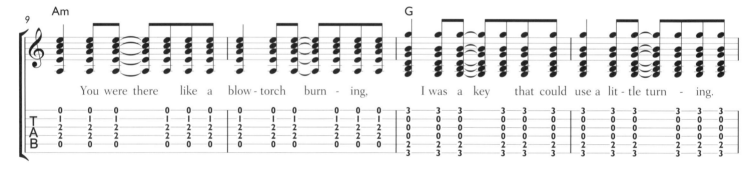

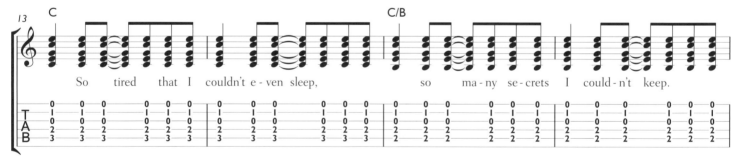

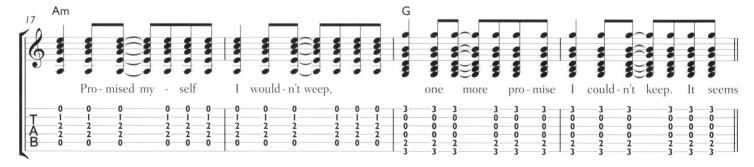

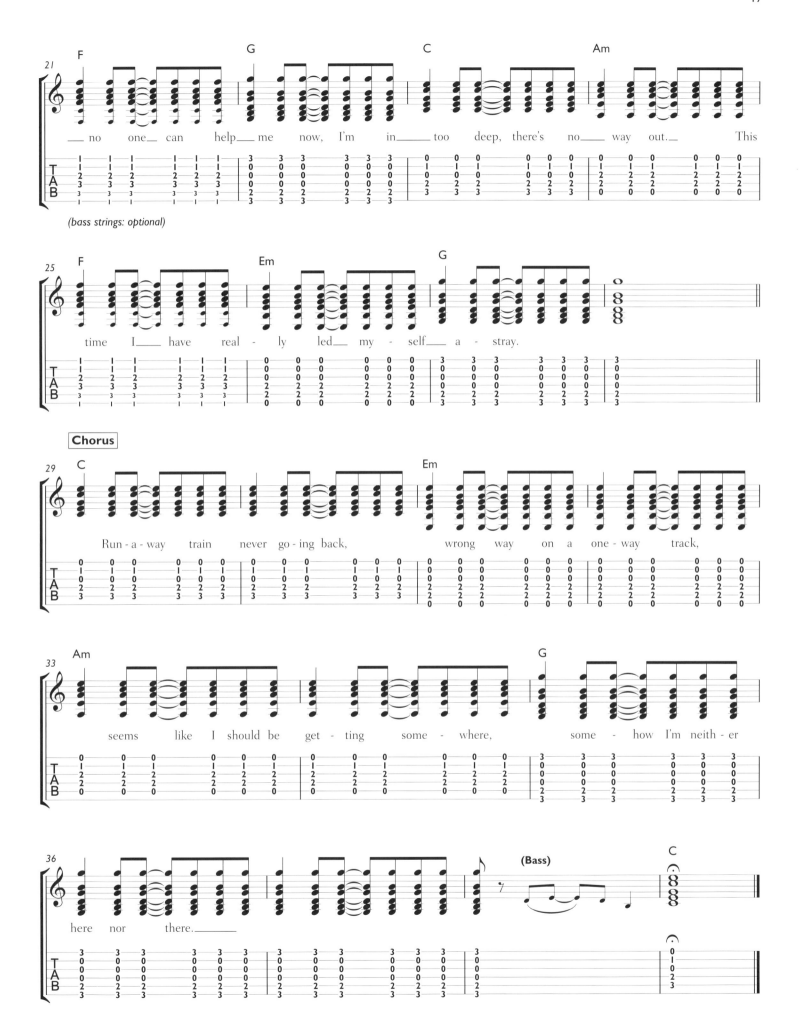

SUNNY AFTERNOON

Words and Music by Ray Davies

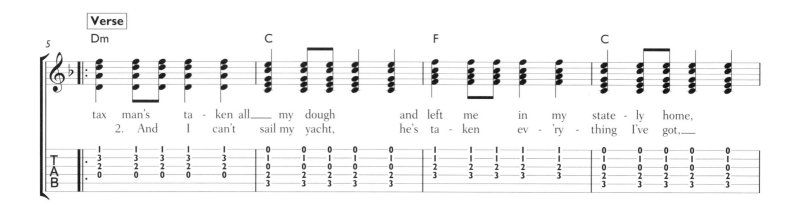

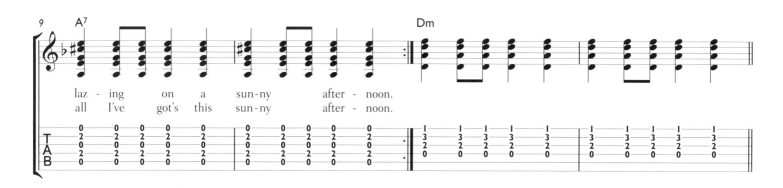

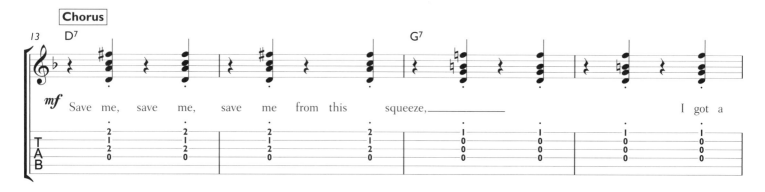

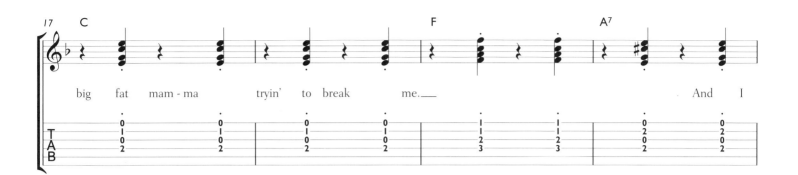

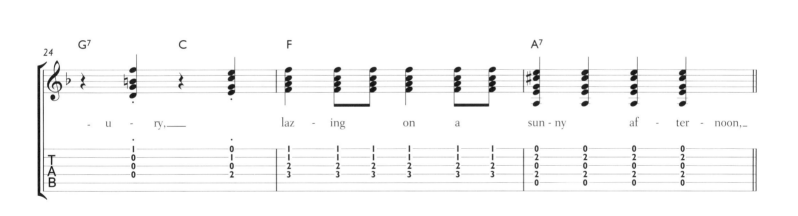

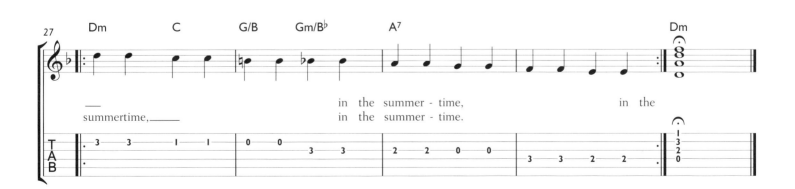

TAKE IT EASY

Words and Music by Glenn Frey and Jackson Browne

♩ = 110 **Country Rock** *2 bars count-in*

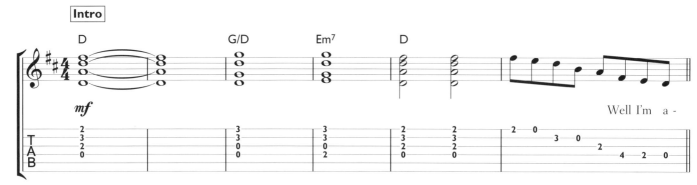

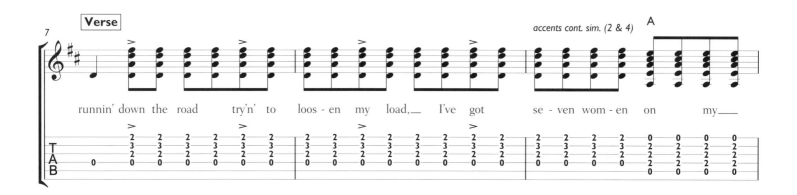

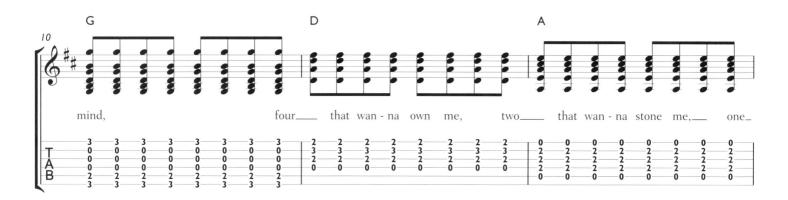

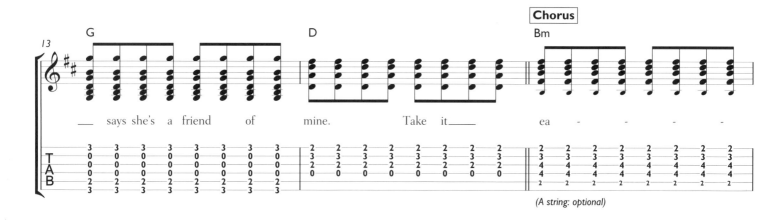

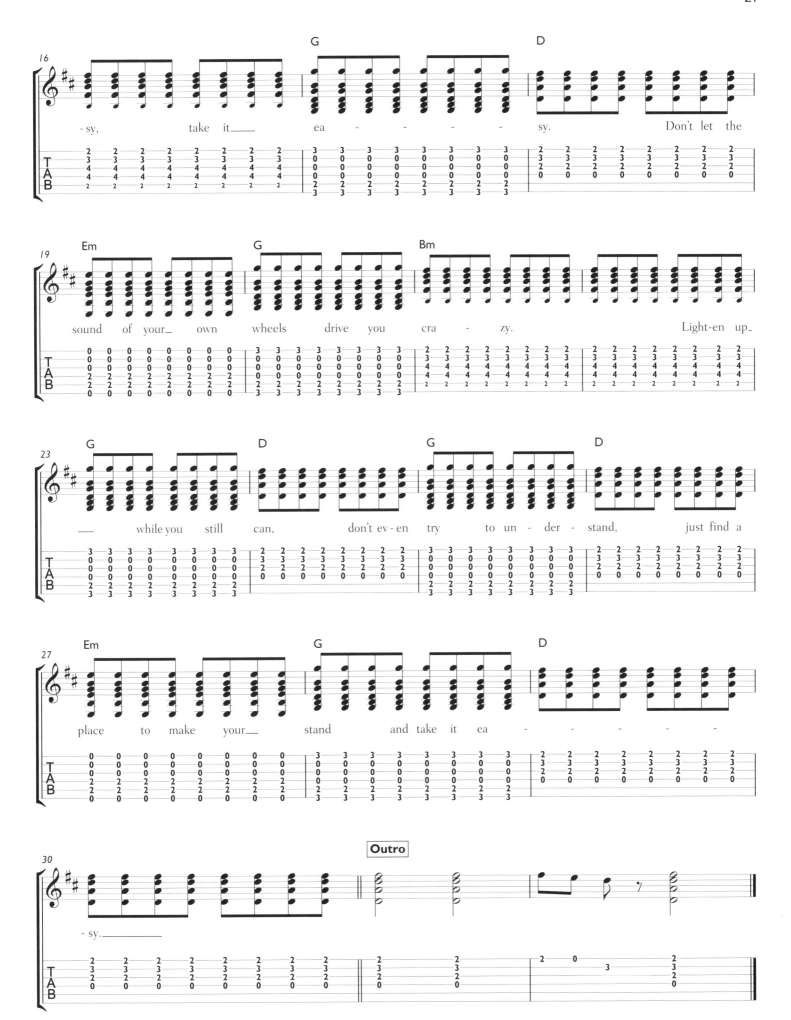

Demo 20
BT 21

THE TWIST

Words and Music by Hank Ballard

♩ = 140 **Rock N Roll** *2 bars count-in*

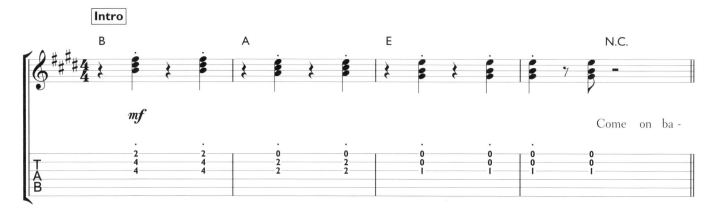

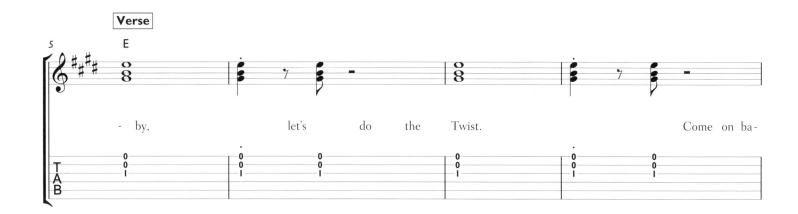

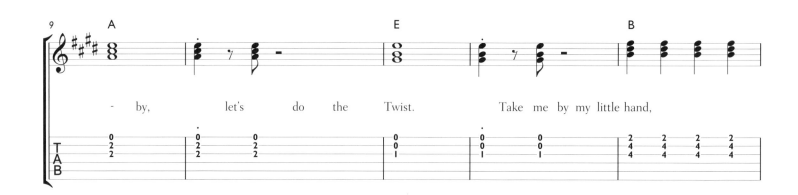

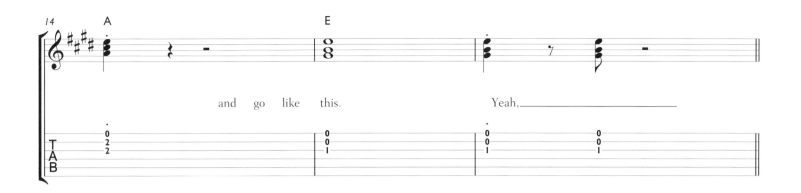

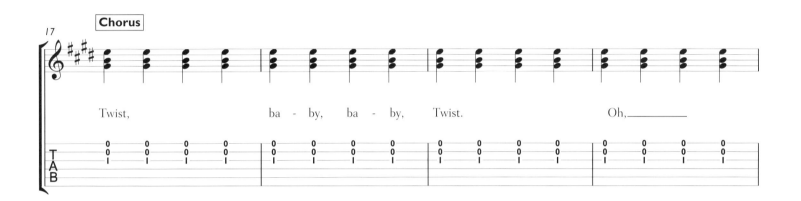

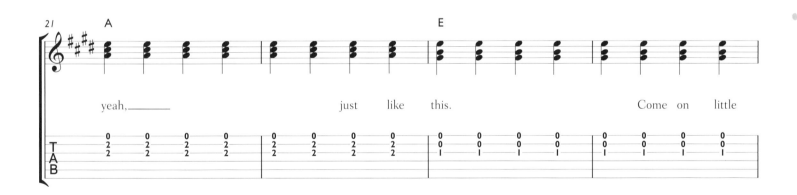

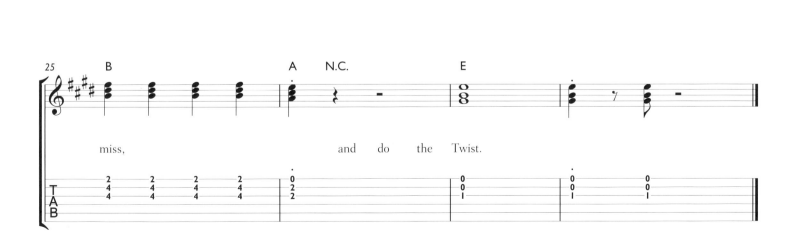